CO-ASI-265

FRACTAL ART BY HEINZ WOLF

This book is dedicated

to my mother and father

Anna Gudac Messick, and John Messick.

Special thanks to

Paul and Elisabeth Butkovich

for providing the inspiration for this book.

IYWAY
COMPANY L.L.C.

7754 WISE
RICHMOND HEIGHTS
MISSOURI, 63117
314-644-5751

IyedoVille

A Nursery Rhyme Book

By Robert E. Messick

IyedoVille Story

From the planet Fracto, in the Big Bopper Galaxy
came two travelers condemned for speaking fallacy.

As pleas of mercy fell upon his ears The Great Googa
Mooga banished them for gooda.

Iye and Iyedo flew through space without a home,
without a place.

They came upon a planet blue with plants and
flowers of every hue.

And as they circled, both
could see that this little
planet held the key.

The key to open up our
eyes to all the mysteries
held inside.

As they steered their
ship upon a beam they
came upon a pleasant
scene.

A town called Wood
River looked just great to settle in and populate.

At 19 Haller, an abandoned home gave them reason
to never roam.

The people of Wood River took them in and treated them
like next of kin.

Potentates & Hot n' Tots
greeted these two Bop-shee-bops.

With feelings of love and none of hate
they gave them space to integrate.

Citizens offered their hearts to fill
as the mayor proclaimed it IyedoVille.

They brought with them a way of seeing,
and rhymes would show us that seeing is believing.

What Do You Think I Am?

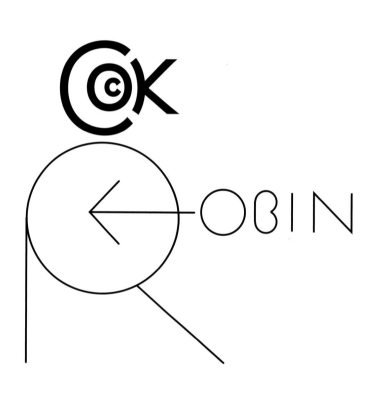

Cock Robin

A little cock sparrow sat on a green tree,

And he chirruped, he chirruped, so merry was he.

A naughty boy came with his wee bow and arrow,

Says he, I will shoot this little cock sparrow;

His body will make me a nice little stew,

And his giblets will make me a little pie too.

Oh, no, said the sparrow, I won't make a stew,

So he clapped his wings and away he flew.

Who Do You Think I Am?

THERE WAS A FAT MAN FROM BOMBAY

There Was a Fat Man
From Bombay

As a little fat man of Bombay

Was smoking one very hot day,

A bird called a snipe

Flew away with his pipe,

Which vexed the fat man of Bombay.

What Do You Think I Am?

Donkey

If I had a donkey that wouldn't go,

Would I beat him? Oh no, no.

I'd put him in the barn and give him some corn,

The best little donkey that ever was born.

Songs they heard on their
ship's receiver,

Filled their heads with
jungle fever.

The words and sounds
seemed quite maddening,

As they soon prepared for
an earthly landing.

The midnight earth walk
was fraught with tension,

And could not mask their
apprehension.

Songs of monsters
consuming human stew,

Filled the heads of these
frightened two.

Disturbing sounds
with odd rhyme and
strange meter,

It was a one-eyed
one-horned flying purple
people eater.

13

Who Do You Think I Am?

Harry Parry

Oh, rare Harry Parry,

When will you marry?

When apples and pears are ripe.

I'll come to your wedding

Without any bidding,

And dance and sing all the night.

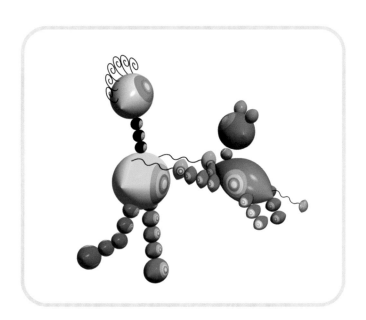

What Do You Think I Am?

Hen

I had a little hen,

　　The prettiest ever seen;

She washed up the dishes,

　　And kept the house clean.

She went to the mill

　　To fetch me some flour,

And always got home

　　In less than an hour.

She baked me my bread,

　　She brewed me my ale,

She sat by the fire

　　And told a fine tale.

What Am I?

I Had A
Little Horse

I had a little horse,

His name was Dappled Grey,

His head was made of gingerbread,

His tail was made of hay:

He could amble, he could trot,

He could carry the mustard pot,

He could amble, he could trot,

Through the old Town of Windsor.

Ham and eggs served with flare,

On Saturday night a small-town fare.

Iye and Iyedo lost in vision,

Hear Baabaaloo beats from the television.

Who Do You Think I Am?

Jacky

When Jacky's a good boy,

    He shall have cakes and custard;

But when he does nothing but cry,

    He shall have nothing but mustard.

What Do You Think I Am?

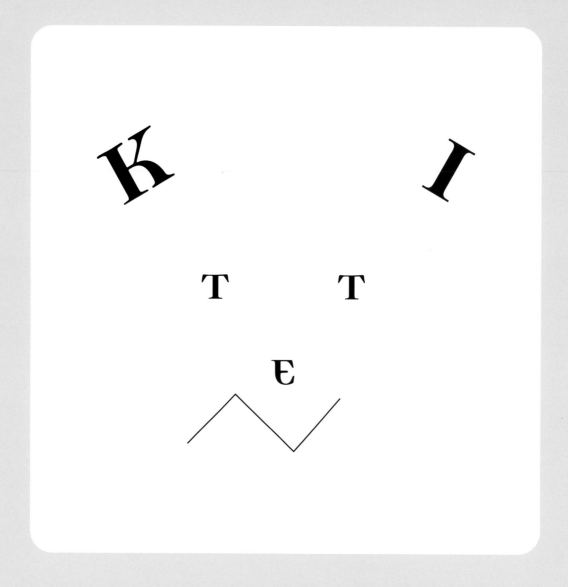

Kitten

Three little kittens they lost their mittens,

 And they began to cry,

Oh, mother dear, we sadly fear

 That we have lost our mittens.

What! lost your mittens, you naughty kittens!

 Then you shall have no pie.

 Mee-ow, mee-ow, mee-ow.

 No, you shall have no pie.

The three little kittens they found their mittens,

 And they began to cry,

Oh, mother dear, see here, see here,

 For we have found our mittens.

Put on your mittens, you silly kittens,

 And you shall have some pie.

Who Am I?

Robin Hood

Robin Hood, Robin Hood,
 Is in the mickle wood;
Little John, Little John,
 He to the town is gone.

Robin Hood, Robin Hood,
 Is telling his beads,
All in the green wood,
 Among the green weeds.

Little John, Little John,
 If he comes no more,
Robin Hood, Robin Hood,
 He will fret full sore.

The Mid-town feature
. . . an odd-looking creature.

This sci-fi flick soon
drenched the screen,
With shining scales of
slimy green.

A black lagoon filled the
theater room with waves
and waves of chilling doom.

And as they walked home
they felt a foreboding,

Said one to the other
"We'll never go boating."

What Do You Think I Am?

Ring o' Roses

Ring-a-ring o' roses,

A pocket full of posies,

A-tishoo! A-tishoo!

We all fall down.

What Am I?

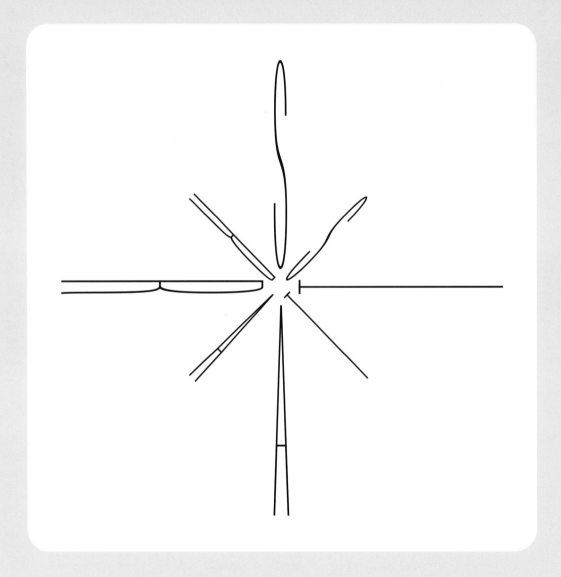

The Star

Twinkle, twinkle, little star,
How I wonder what you are!
Up above the world so high,
Like a diamond in the sky.

When the blazing sun is gone,
When he nothing shines upon,
Then you show your little light,
Twinkle, twinkle, all the night.

What Do You Think I Am?

Wind

Blow, wind, blow! and go, mill, go!

That the miller may grind his corn;

That the baker may take it,

And into bread make it,

And bring us a loaf in the morn.

A teen town called Jiveland had them quite perplexed,
Our interstellar fellas were a little vexed.

All that dancing seemed to have no meaning.
Yet as twilight turned into evening,

Iye and Iyedo were a' rocking and a' reeling.

What Do You Think I Am?

World

If all the world were paper,

And all the sea were ink,

If all the trees were bread and cheese,

What should we have to drink?

Who Am I?

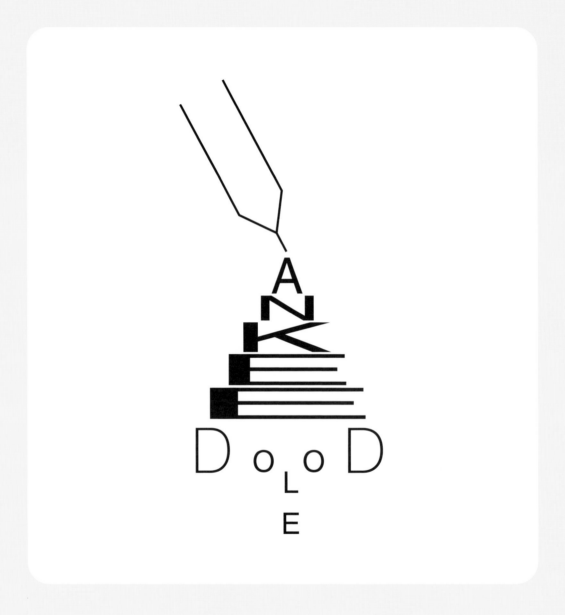

Yankee Doodle

Yankee Doodle came to town,

Riding on a pony;

He stuck a feather in his cap

And called it macaroni.

Across the street from Wood River High
Is a root beer stand under a cerulean sky.

Drinking root beer, looking cool,
Iye and Iyedo sitting on a Blevin's stool.

They slowly sipped with deliberation.
A frosty, sweet, nonalcoholic libation.

"Living in the you s hay."